Introduction

Here it is – my very first joke book!
I hope you like it.
In fact I hope you laugh so much your socks
come zooming off your feet like rockets.
You will find even more than jokes in here too!
There are snippets from many of the stories
I've written, PLUS a brand-new two-part tale
about those daft Indoor Pirates.
Enjoy!

☆ ☆ ☆ ☆

PUFFIN BOOKS

Jeremy Strong once worked in a bakery, putting the jam into three thousand doughnuts every night. Now he puts the jam in stories instead, which he finds much more exciting. At the age of three, he fell out of a first-floor bedroom window and landed on his head. His mother says that this damaged him for the rest of his life and refuses to take any responsibility. He loves writing stories because he says it is 'the only time you alone have complete control and can make anything happen'. His ambition is to make you laugh (or at least snuffle). Jeremy Strong lives near Bath with his wife, Gillie, four cats and a flying cow.

Are you feeling silly enough to read more?

THE BEAK SPEAKS
CHICKEN SCHOOL
DINOSAUR POX
GIANT JIM AND THE HURRICANE
I'M TELLING YOU, THEY'RE ALIENS!
THE INDOOR PIRATES
THE INDOOR PIRATES ON TREASURE ISLAND
THE KARATE PRINCESS
THE KARATE PRINCESS AND THE LAST GRIFFIN
THE KARATE PRINCESS TO THE RESCUE
THE KARATE PRINCESS IN MONSTA TROUBLE
KRAZY KOW SAVES THE WORLD – WELL, ALMOST
LET'S DO THE PHARAOH!
PANDEMONIUM AT SCHOOL
PIRATE PANDEMONIUM
THE SHOCKING ADVENTURES OF LIGHTNING LUCY
THERE'S A PHARAOH IN OUR BATH!
THERE'S A VIKING IN MY BED
TROUBLE WITH ANIMALS
VIKING AT SCHOOL
VIKING IN TROUBLE

Read more about Streaker's adventures:
THE HUNDRED-MILE-AN-HOUR DOG
RETURN OF THE HUNDRED-MILE-AN-HOUR DOG
WANTED! THE HUNDRED-MILE-AN-HOUR DOG
LOST! THE HUNDRED-MILE-AN-HOUR DOG

Read more about Nicholas's daft family:
MY DAD'S GOT AN ALLIGATOR!
MY GRANNY'S GREAT ESCAPE
MY MUM'S GOING TO EXPLODE!
MY BROTHER'S FAMOUS BOTTOM
MY BROTHER'S FAMOUS BOTTOM GETS PINCHED
MY BROTHER'S FAMOUS BOTTOM GOES CAMPING

Jeremy STRONG'S

LAUGH-YOUR-SOCKS-OFF

PUFFIN

PUFFIN BOOKS

Published by the Penguin Group
Penguin Books Ltd, 80 Strand, London WC2R 0RL, England
Penguin Group (USA) Inc., 375 Hudson Street,
New York, New York 10014, USA
Penguin Group (Canada), 90 Eglinton Avenue East, Suite 700,
Toronto, Ontario, Canada M4P 2Y3
(a division of Pearson Penguin Canada Inc.)
Penguin Ireland, 25 St Stephen's Green, Dublin 2, Ireland
(a division of Penguin Books Ltd)
Penguin Group (Australia), 250 Camberwell Road, Camberwell,
Victoria 3124, Australia (a division of Pearson Australia Group Pty Ltd)
Penguin Books India Pvt Ltd, 11 Community Centre, Panchsheel Park,
New Delhi – 110 017, India
Penguin Group (NZ), 67 Apollo Drive, Rosedale, North Shore 0632,
New Zealand (a division of Pearson New Zealand Ltd)
Penguin Books (South Africa) (Pty) Ltd, 24 Sturdee Avenue, Rosebank,
Johannesburg 2196, South Africa

Penguin Books Ltd, Registered Offices:
80 Strand, London WC2R 0RL, England

puffinbooks.com

First published 2008
008

Set in Sabon, Ad Lib, Bokka and Magicpants
Made and printed in England by Clays Ltd, St Ives plc

British Library Cataloguing in Publication Data
A CIP catalogue record for this book is available from the British Library

ISBN: 978–0–141–32513–2

www.greenpenguin.co.uk

Penguin Books is committed to a sustainable future for our business, our readers and our planet. This book is made from Forest Stewardship Council™ certified paper.

Contents

Hundred-Mile-an-Hour Hilarity

Meet Trevor. He's the owner of Streaker, a rocket on four legs with a woof attached! Streaker's the fastest dog in the world – and she's also pretty quick at getting into trouble. Poor old 'Trevor Two-Legs' (as Streaker calls him) is always having to get himself and the Hundred-Mile-An-Hour Dog out of scrapes. But he wouldn't have it any other way!

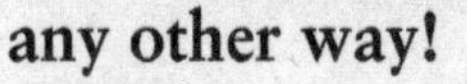

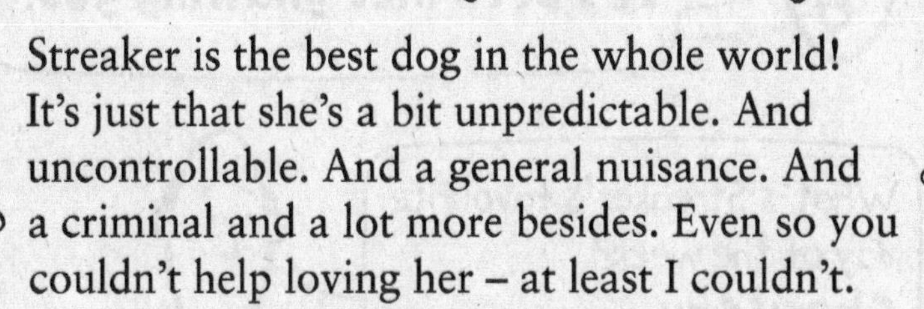

Streaker is the best dog in the whole world! It's just that she's a bit unpredictable. And uncontrollable. And a general nuisance. And a criminal and a lot more besides. Even so you couldn't help loving her – at least I couldn't.

Wanted! The Hundred-Mile-an-Hour Dog

What happened when Streaker ate ten plates of baked beans?
She ran like the wind.

What's Streaker's favourite food?
Fast food, of course!

What's Streaker's second favourite food?
Anything that's on your plate.

What did Streaker say to her bone?
'It's been nice gnawing you!'

What's Streaker's favourite day of the week?
Chewsday.

What happened when Streaker ate a bag of garlic?
Her bark was definitely worse than her bite.

What should you do if Streaker eats your pencil?
Use a pen instead.

What happened when Streaker saw the sign saying 'Wet Paint'?
That's exactly what she did!

Trevor, do dogs wear knickers?

Well in the summer, Streaker wears a collar and pants.

Did you realize that Streaker has been barking all night!!!

Oh, don't worry, she's getting plenty of sleep during the day.

Can you please stop Streaker from barking in your back garden?!

OK. I'll put her in the front garden.

What's the difference between Streaker and a leaky tap?
None – they both keep running.

Why does Streaker keep scratching herself?
She's the only one that knows where it itches.

What does Trevor read to Streaker at night?
A bite-time story.

What kind of stories does Streaker like best?
Furry tales.

What does Streaker do when she's watching a DVD?
She presses 'Paws'.

How does Streaker keep in touch with her furry friends?
By mobile bone.

Why would Streaker like to be a police-dog?
She could follow some interesting leads.

Why would Streaker make a terrible police-dog?
She's always barking up the wrong tree.

Why doesn't Streaker drive a car?
She can never find a barking space.

Oh no, I've lost Streaker!

Well, why don't you put an advert in the paper?

Don't be stupid, Streaker can't read!

Streaker Scramble

All these mixed-up words are parts of Streaker's body. Can you unscramble them and draw lines to the right bits of her body?

Streaker Shapes

Look carefully at these pictures of Streaker. Can you match each picture to the right shadow on the page opposite? Draw lines to make pairs.

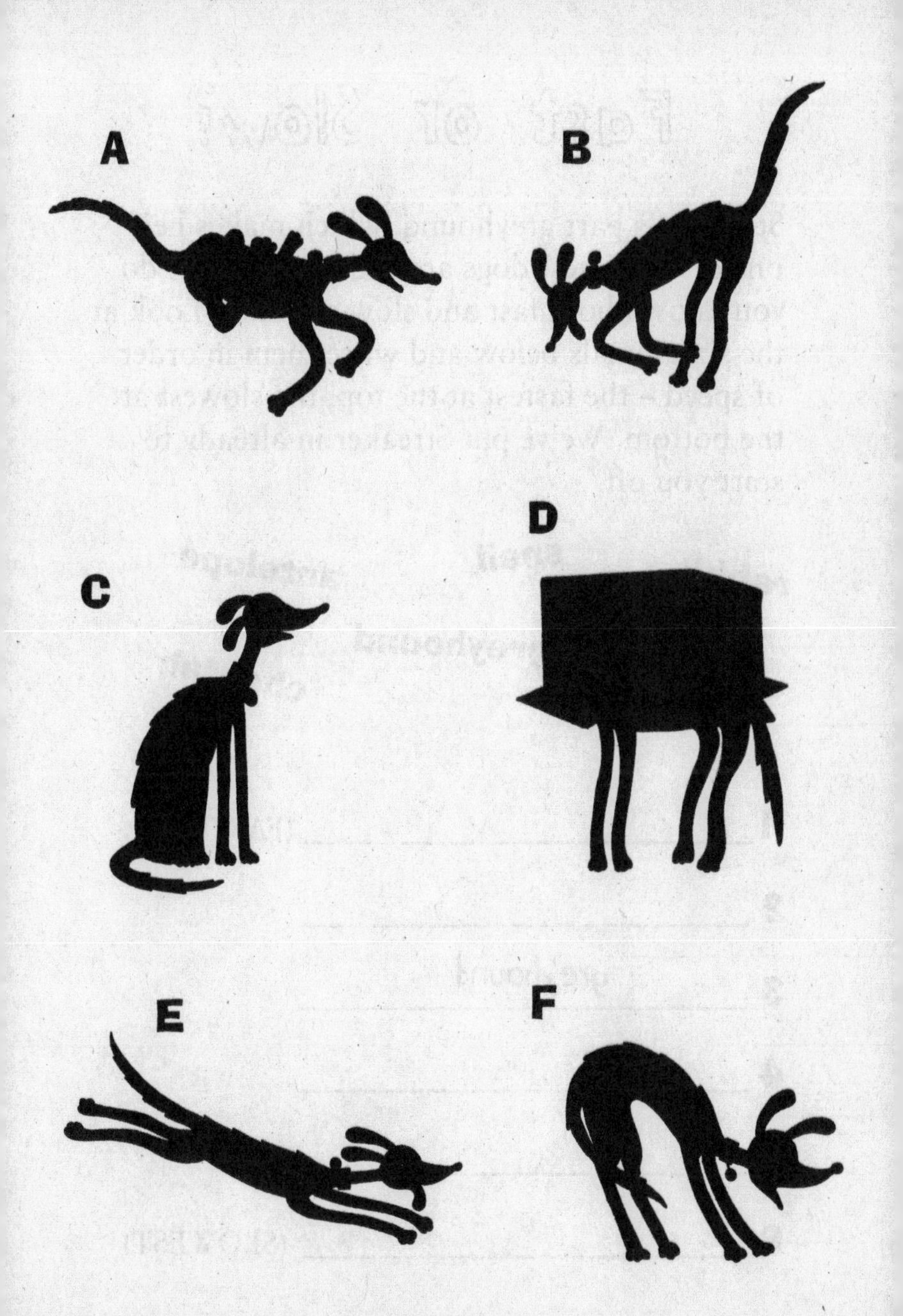
A
B
C
D
E
F

Fast or Slow?

Streaker is part greyhound, which makes her one of the fastest dogs around! How much do you know about fast and slow animals? Look at the six animals below and write them in order of speed – the fastest at the top, the slowest at the bottom. We've put Streaker in already to start you off.

rabbit **snail** **antelope**

tortoise **greyhound** **cheetah**

1 ______________________ (FASTEST)

2 ______________________

3 greyhound

4 ______________________

5 ______________________

6 ______________________ (SLOWEST)

Animal Antics

Dynamite dogs aren't the only animals causing havoc. In *The Trouble with Animals* there's a whole host of creatures, including foxes, rabbits, donkeys and even a penguin. And in *The Beak Speaks* Dinah the mynah bird, along with a helpful chimpanzee called Arnold Teabag, foil the evil Divine's plans to make money out of a houseful of captive wild animals.

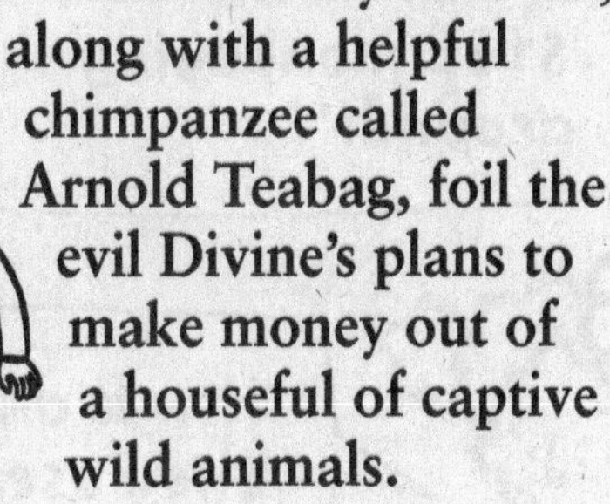

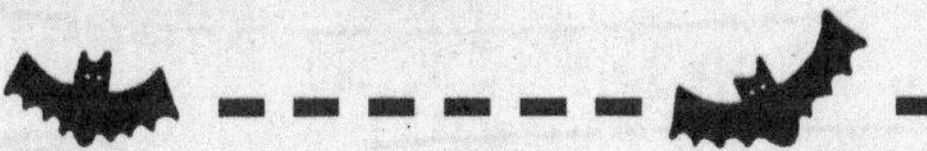

There was a chimp sitting on the floor with our coffee table on his head. He was covered in soot and a big sooty trail led all the way from the fireplace to where he was sitting.

'Hello,' I said, like you do when you meet a chimp with a table on his head. Dinah and the chimp stared at me. He lifted one leg and . . . well, piffed, noisily. Dinah gave a small choking noise and slowly toppled backwards off her perch.

The Beak Speaks

What do chimpanzees like to eat?
Chocolate chimp cookies.

What did one chimpanzee say to the other?
'Stop monkeying around!'

How do chimps make toast?
They use a gorilla.

What's invisible and smells likes bananas?
Chimpanzee burps.

Can chimpanzees fly?
No — only hot air baboons.

What's a chimpanzee's favourite month?
Ape-ril.

Where do mynah birds go to eat?
In a nestaurant.

What do you get if you cross a mynah bird and a centipede?
A walkie-talkie.

What happened when the fox got arrested?
He had a brush with the law.

If a fox lost his tail, where would he get another one?
At a re-tail store.

What do you get if you cross a rabbit with a bee?
A honey bunny.

What do you get if a rabbit sits on your head?
A bad hare day.

What is a twip?
What a wabbit takes when he wides a twain.

What do rabbits do when they get married?
Go on a bunnymoon.

How can you tell the difference between a rabbit and a red-eyed monster?
Try getting a red-eyed monster into a rabbit hutch!

Why do rabbits have shiny noses?
Because their powder puffs are at the other end.

What do you call a donkey with three legs?
A wonkey.

What do you call a one-eyed donkey with three legs?
A winky wonkey.

Why did the donkey feel stupid?
He'd made a complete ass of himself.

What did the mummy donkey say to the baby donkey?
'Eeyore carrots up!'

What do you call a penguin in the desert?
Lost.

What do mummy penguins say to their children if they go out in the dark?
'Beak careful out there.'

What's black and white and goes round and round?
A penguin in a revolving door.

What's black and white and red all over?
A penguin with sunburn.

Animal Wordsnake

Evil Divine has been keeping lots of animals caged up in her house so she can sell them at a profit! Can you find the animals in the wordsnake opposite? Using a pencil (in case you make a mistake) trace the words, which are in the order shown below. The words form a continuous line, snaking up and down, backwards and forwards, but never diagonally.

~~FROG~~
SPIDER
BIRD
HYENA
VULTURE
CHIMPANZEE
HIPPO
BAT
RABBIT

F	R	I	B	B
G	O	T	R	A
S	P	I	T	A
I	B	D	O	B
R	R	E	P	P
D	H	Y	H	I
A	N	E	E	E
V	R	E	N	Z
U	U	C	A	P
L	T	H	I	M

Puppies, Kittens and More . . .

Can you match the baby animals below to their grown-up parents?

1	dog	**a**	fawn
2	donkey	**b**	kitten
3	deer	**c**	cub
4	elephant	**d**	puppy
5	fox	**e**	kid
6	spider	**f**	chick
7	bird	**g**	foal
8	cat	**h**	spiderling
9	goat	**i**	calf

Dippy Dinosaurs

Jodie is fed up. She hates her horrible hair and freckles. She wishes she could change. Then one morning she wakes up only to discover that she has turned into a stegosaurus! And she's not sure if she likes the change . . .

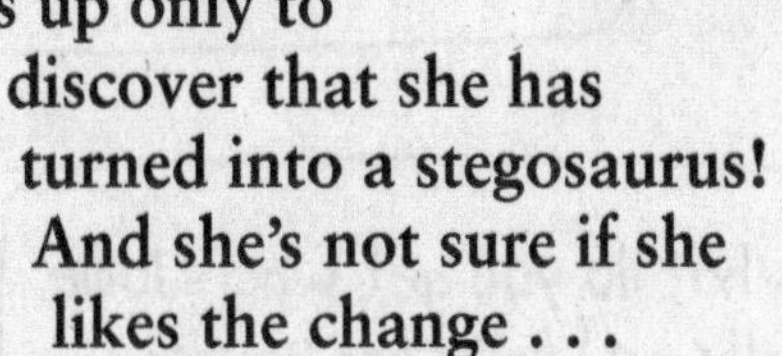

It was a dinosaur that got out of bed the next day – a dinosaur with fat, stumpy legs like thick tree trunks. Instead of freckles she had purple and green blotches all over her fat, scaly body. She had a long thick tail. She had great leathery plates sticking out of her back, like fins that had been designed by somebody who couldn't draw. She had a small head with little red glinting eyes, a long snout and an even longer thick purple tongue.

Dinosaur Pox

What happened when Jodie fell over?
She was dino-sore!

What happens when Jodie goes to sleep?
She becomes a stego-snorus.

What do you get when Jodie talks and talks for hours?
A dinobore.

What kind of tool does Jodie use?
A dino-saw.

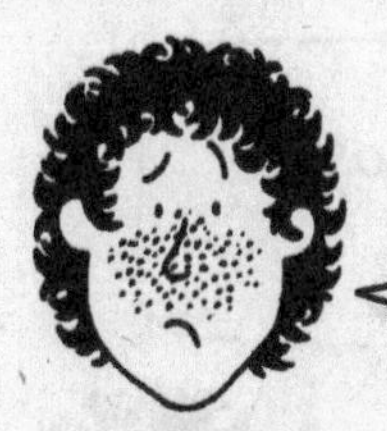

What do you call a dinosaur who smashes everything up?
Tyrannosaurus wrecks.

What's the best way to talk to a T-rex?
From a very long distance.

What do you call a T-rex with bananas in its ears?
Anything you like – it can't hear you!

What do you get when a T-rex sneezes?
Out of the way!

Which is the scariest dinosaur?
The terror-dactyl.

What did dinosaurs have that no other animals have?
Baby dinosaurs.

What do you call a dinosaur who never gives up?
A try-try-try-ceratops.

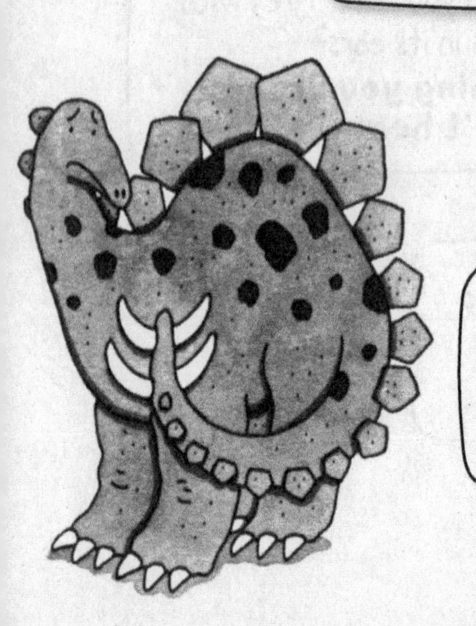

Why are dinosaurs healthier than dragons?
Because dinosaurs don't smoke.

Dino True or False

Are you a dino expert? Read the sentences below, then tick the true or false box.

1 Dinosaurs are extinct.

☐ TRUE ☐ FALSE

2 Some dinosaurs were as small as chickens.

☐ TRUE ☐ FALSE

3 Scientists don't know what colour dinosaurs were.

☐ TRUE ☐ FALSE

4 Humans lived at the same time as dinosaurs.

☐ TRUE ☐ FALSE

5 Some dinosaurs ate only plants.

☐ TRUE ☐ FALSE

6 Scientists have now discovered all the different kinds of dinosaur that once existed.

☐ TRUE ☐ FALSE

Dino-words

How many words can you make from the word:

DINOSAUR?

Write your words in the space below.

Dinosaur Match

Jodie's brother Mark knew immediately that she had turned into a stegosaurus! But can you tell a tyrannosaur from a triceratops? Read the dinosaur descriptions below and see if you can match them to the right pictures.

1 This dinosaur had sharp horns on its head and nose.

2 This dinosaur had a spiky tail and lots of hard bony plates running from its head to its tail.

3 This dinosaur was enormous, with a long tail. It ate only plants.

4 This dinosaur had very sharp teeth that enabled it to kill its prey quickly.

The Indoor Pirates and Heart-Ripper-crunch-Munch-Smelly-Belly-Bum-Biter-Cuddles

Part One: An unpleasant surprise

The Indoor Pirates had been out shopping and now they were on their way home in Captain Blackpatch's truck. The truck was blood red, which was the captain's favourite colour. Blackpatch had made the garage man paint a skull and crossbones on the side. The truck also had a Jolly Roger flying from the cabin.

Lumpy Lawson, Bald Ben and the twins Molly and Polly had to sit in the back because there were only two seats in the front and the captain was the driver. The passenger seat was always taken up by an anchor. (If you're wondering why he had an anchor there, you are about to find out.)

And if you want to know why the pirates went around in a truck I will tell you. They didn't like water and they didn't like boats. So they stayed indoors most of the time, in their house: number 25 Dolphin Street. That's why they were called the Indoor Pirates, of course. Everybody knows that!

Polly and Molly were arguing, as usual.

'I'm going faster than you!' said Polly.

'No, I'm going faster than you!' yelled Molly.

'Don't be daft. You can't go faster than me because we're both in the same truck!' cried Polly triumphantly.

'I KNOW THAT!' declared Molly. 'And anyhow, guess what? I'm going slower than you, so there, nurr with knobs on.' She put her fingers in her ears. 'And now I can't hear so I don't know what you're saying. La la la la.' And she sang the rest of the way home.

Polly sat opposite her sister and pulled faces at her.

Molly closed her eyes. 'I can't see you either,' she said, interrupting her singing for a second or two before carrying on. 'La la la la . . .'

Lumpy Lawson and Bald Ben heaved a sigh of relief when the captain at last turned into Dolphin Street. The truck went zooming down the road at great speed and just before they reached number 25, Captain Blackpatch rolled down his window and chucked out the anchor. He had never learned what brakes were for.

The anchor bounced along the road several times, caught round a tree and a moment later they were jerked to a halt.

'Right,' declared the captain. 'Everyone help get the shopping into the house.' They began to unload the car.

'My bag's bigger than your bag,' said Polly.

'My bag is bigger AND heavier than yours,' declared Molly. 'So knickers to you.'

'Well,' smirked Polly, 'your knickers are even bigger than your bag, because you have got such a gigantic big –'

'AARGH!' Captain Blackpatch gave a terrible cry and Polly never finished. The captain was standing at the open front door and staring into the house with horror.

'We've been burgled!' he cried.

'Robbed!' gasped Bald Ben. 'Who would want to do a nasty thing like that?'

Captain Blackpatch gave Ben a dark look. 'Ben, we are pirates. *We're* supposed to rob people – and now *we've* been robbed instead. It's not right at all.'

They stared at the mess the burglars had left behind. The sofa was upside down and had an armchair perched on top of it. Cushions lay everywhere. Vases had been smashed. Drawers had been pulled out and emptied on to the floor. Curtains had been torn from the windows. It was a sorry sight.

'We've been stolened,' said Polly.

'Can't say stolened, stupid. You have to say stolen,' snapped Molly.

'But *we* haven't been stolen. *We're* here. It's what's gone that's been stolen,' said Polly.

'Nasty, horrible thieves!' shouted Lumpy Lawson, shaking a knobbly fist at nothing in particular. 'If only I could get my hands on them I'd put them in my biggest frying pan and sizzle 'em until they jumped all over the place.'

'What are we going to do?' they chorused and everyone looked expectantly at Captain Blackpatch. He tugged at his beard thoughtfully. His eyes narrowed.

'What we need is a plan!' he declared. 'Exactly. A plan. That's what we need.' And the others looked at Captain Blackpatch even more expectantly. He tugged his beard even harder.

'And the plan is –' he began, rolling his eyes

from side to side as he scoured his head for an idea – 'the plan is that I shall go upstairs to think and when I come down I shall tell you what the plan is.'

Bald Ben scratched the tattoo on top of his bald head. (It was picture of a rose, with I LOVE MUM written underneath.) 'I don't think that will work,' said Bald Ben.

'What do you mean?' Captain Blackpatch eyed him suspiciously.

'Well, your plan is that you'll go upstairs to think and your other plan is that you'll come down and tell us what it is. You can't come down and tell us that the plan is that you'll go upstairs and then come down and tell us what the plan is, because the plan is that you'll go upstairs to think and then you'll come down and you'll spend all day just going up stairs and coming down again to tell us you're going up and –'

'SHUT UP!' roared Captain Blackpatch. 'You're all idiots. Am I the only one with a brain here?'

'Polly doesn't have a brain –' began Molly.

'DON'T YOU START!' warned the captain, giving the twins a black look. 'I'm going upstairs to think, and you lot can put the shopping away AND tidy up this horrible mess.' He clumped up the stairs and disappeared from sight.

While the remaining pirates unpacked the bags, put all the shopping away AND cleared up the mess, Captain Blackpatch stayed upstairs thinking. The others knew he must be thinking very hard because they could hear his snores even from down below.

They stared at the mess the burglars had left behind them and wondered where to start. Newspapers, plastic seagulls, letters, table lamps, eyepatches, shoes, wooden legs, toys, underpants, hooks, seaboots, bits of food, stuffed parrots and dirty plates had been thrown higgledy-piggledy all over the place and in every room. It was going to take hours to sort out. And all that time the captain stayed upstairs, thinking.

It was four hours before Captain Blackpatch reappeared, but when he did he was wearing a broad smile.

'I have solved our problem,' he announced. 'What we need is a guard dog, a very fierce guard dog, that will bark loudly if burglars ever come again.'

'Yes!' cried Lumpy Lawson. 'And it can growl at them and show them big sharp teeth.'

'And it can run after the burglars and bite their bottoms!' shouted Molly.

'It can bite *your* bottom!' giggled Polly.

'Bite yours first,' snapped Molly.

Bald Ben put his hand up. He had a question. The last time Bald Ben had asked a question he'd got Captain Blackpatch into a big muddle. The captain frowned.

'What is it?' he hissed.

'I was just wondering, where will we get a guard dog from?'

'A guard dog shop, you big, bouncing baldie!'

yelled the captain. 'A pet shop. There's one in town. Come on.'

So they piled back in the truck, drove off at high speed and immediately came to a crunching halt. The captain's hat fell over his eyes. Lumpy Lawson spilled his drink and the twins banged their heads.

'OW!' yelled Molly.

'My OW! is bigger than your OW!' squeaked Polly.

'No, my OW! is as big as the biggest head bump on the planet!' countered Molly.

'And MY OW! is as big as the biggest bump on the biggest planet in the biggest universe in the biggest ever whatever!' squawked Polly triumphantly. 'So there.'

Molly gave her sister a poisonous smile. 'Yes,' she agreed. 'But that's because you're as stupid as the biggest ever whatever, so there – multiplied.'

Bald Ben got out and enjoyed the silence outside the truck for a few moments before he unwound the anchor from the tree. Off they went once more and this time they actually reached the pet shop.

The Indoor Pirates stood outside and Captain Blackpatch rubbed his hands with glee. 'We are going to get the best guard dog ever,' he crowed. 'Come on! Let's get inside!'

Will Captain Blackpatch's plan work?
Probably not!
You can find out what happens next
by reading Part Two on page 76.

Pirate Pandemonium

At Witts End Primary School, there's shiploads of swashbuckling fun when the new supply teacher, Miss Pandemonium, lets her class be pirates for the whole of Book Week. While over at Pirate School, the fiercest head teacher to sail the seven seas, Patagonia Clatterbottom, is giving lessons in walking the plank and shivering ye timbers! Yo ho ho!

Pirates did a lot of kidnapping and marooning and holding people to ransom. They used to board ships and seize all their gold and jewels and then they'd sail off to secret islands and bury their ill-gotten gains.

'Sounds good to me,' grinned Samantha.

Pirate Pandemonium

What happens at pirate school lunchtime?
Everyone slurps soup on the sloop.

What's for the main course?
Fish and ships.

What's the pirate kids' favourite dessert?
Jelly Roger.

What does the school parrot eat?
Polyfilla.

Where does the pirate teacher keep the paints and paper?
In the arrrrrrrt cupboard.

How does the teacher get everything so cheaply?
She waits for the sail.

How do you spell 'galleon'?

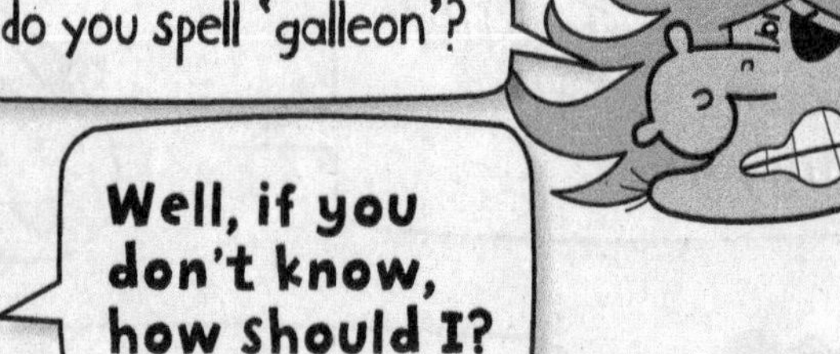

Well, if you don't know, how should I?

Why is your phone going *beep, beep, beep*?

I must have left it off the hook.

What's the name of the pirate school librarian?
Captain Book.

Where do pirate kids go to the toilet?
On the poop deck.

What's the pirate kids' favourite book?
Booty and the Beast.

Why couldn't the pirate kids play cards?
The teacher was standing on the deck.

Why don't pirate kids get hungry on desert islands?
Because of all the sand which is there.

Why do pirate kids carry a bar of soap?
So, if they are ship-wrecked, they can wash themselves to shore.

What do you get if you cross a pie and a rat?
A pie rat.

How much did the pirate pay for his ear piercings?
A buck-an-ear.

How do pirates get from ship to ship?
By taxi crab.

Why wouldn't the pirate say 'Aye, aye, captain'?
Because his captain only had one eye.

What has five eyes, ten ears and five legs?
Five pirates!

Why is it really hard to give up being a pirate?
Because you get hooked.

How does a pirate with two hooks scratch his nose?
Very carefully!

Why is there a 'd' in 'bandana'?
Because without it, pirates would be wearing bananas on their heads.

Crow's-Nest Climb

Can you climb up the rigging to the pirates' crow's-nest? You'll need to complete each pair of three-letter words with just one letter, e.g. T completes the end of SIT and the start of TEN. When you've finished, you'll find out the name of a favourite pirate pet!

Swashbuckling Crossword

Solve the clues to complete this cunning crossword.

ACROSS

3 Pirates need a map to find the hidden _ _ _ _ _ _ _ _.

6 A pirate flag has one of these on it.

DOWN

1 Some pirates have a _ _ _ _ instead of a hand.

2 The name of a pirate sword.

4 Pirates wouldn't be able to sail the seven seas without one of these!

5 Yo ho ho and a bottle of _ _ _!

1 2 3 4 5 6

Pirate Know-How

How much do you know about pirates? Test yourself by filling in the missing letters below. Then fill in the speech bubble with your own sentence.

Things pirates like

1 g_ld

2 r_m

Things pirates wear

3 h_t

4 ey_ p_ _ch

Things pirates do

5 f_gh_

6 s_il

Things pirates say!

Potty Pharaohs

The pharaoh Sennapod, once High King and Ruler of Upper and Lower Egypt, was brought back to life after four thousand years of mummification. Now the ancient Egyptian lives with Ben, Carrie and their parents at 27 Templeton Terrace – who find that life's always exciting with an extra mummy around!

Sennapod was lost. This was hardly surprising. He had been asleep for the last four thousand or so years and the world had changed quite a lot. He seemed to remember being buried deep inside some pyramid, on the edge of a great desert, but this didn't look like a desert at all. There was no sand, no sun, and it was raining.

There's a Pharaoh in our Bath!

When is a piece of wood like Pharaoh Sennapod?
When it's a ruler.

What do you call Sennapod eating a biscuit?
A crumby mummy.

What kind of music does Sennapod like?
Wrap music.

Why did Sennapod fail his exams?
He didn't complete his cursework.

Why is it safe to tell Sennapod your secrets?
Because he'll keep them under wraps.

Why won't Sennapod go on holiday?
He doesn't like to relax and unwind.

Why does Sennapod always look on the bright side?
Because every shroud has a silver lining.

Why is Sennapod so selfish?

Well, he's a bit wrapped up in himself.

What do you call Sennapod when he's driving?
Toot and car man.

Why were the ancient Egyptians confused?
Because their daddies were mummies.

Where do mummies go swimming?
In the Dead Sea.

What is written on the outside of a pyramid?
'Tomb it may concern.'

Were the pyramids built by the Egyptians?
I sphinx so.
Does Sennapod play tennis?
Yes, many Egyptians once served in the pharaoh's court.
What game did Sennapod play when he was a kid?
Mummies and deadies.
Knock-knock.
Who's there?
Pharaoh.
Pharaoh who?
Pharaoh-nuff.

Egyptian Odd-One-Out

Look carefully at the pictures. Can you find one picture in each set of three that is different from the rest?

3a
4a
3b
4b
3c
4c

Sennapod's Treasure Trail

Sennapod is trying to get to the treasure map without Professor Jelly and Grimstone noticing. Can you help him find a way through the maze without disturbing the greedy pair?

Vagrant Vikings

In another crazy historical mix-up, a Viking arrives in the quiet twenty-first century town of Flotby. The Ellis family are astonished to have a big hairy Viking staying with them but they try to make the best of it. No one's quite sure how Sigurd (aka Siggy) got there, but one thing's for sure – having a Viking around certainly makes life interesting!

> The problem was very simple. Siggy had come straight out of the tenth century and into the twenty-first. A lot of things had changed since 900 AD, and Siggy was still trying to get used to them. Meanwhile Mr and Mrs Ellis were still trying to get used to *him*.
>
> *Viking in Trouble*

Why did Siggy the Viking go to the hospital?
He wanted to see a Norse.

Why did Siggy fail his driving test?
He kept using his horns.

How would you feel if Siggy attacked you with a sword?
A bit Thor.

How do Vikings communicate with each other?
By Norse code.

What do you give a seasick Viking?
Plenty of room!

What do you call a Viking librarian?
Erik the very-well-Red.

Why do Vikings shout a lot?
Because their horns don't work.

Where do all the hungry Vikings come from?
Gnaw-way.

Why did the Vikings have such long boats?
They thought it would cut their journey time down.

Are Vikings big and strong?
Yes, they're as tough as old boats.

Viking Word Grid

How much do you know about Vikings? Look at the questions below and write the answers in the grid opposite. You will find the name of a well-known Viking in the vertical box!

1 What a Viking used to fight with. Watch out, it's very sharp!

2 A Viking would protect himself from attack with one of these – it was usually round and brightly coloured.

3 Vikings were famous for invading other lands. They would usually arrive by sea in one of these.

4 What a Viking would wear on his body to protect himself.

5 The famous Viking helmet has two of these sticking out on either side.

6 Viking men had quite a lot of hair and they would usually have a _ _ _ _ _ on their face.

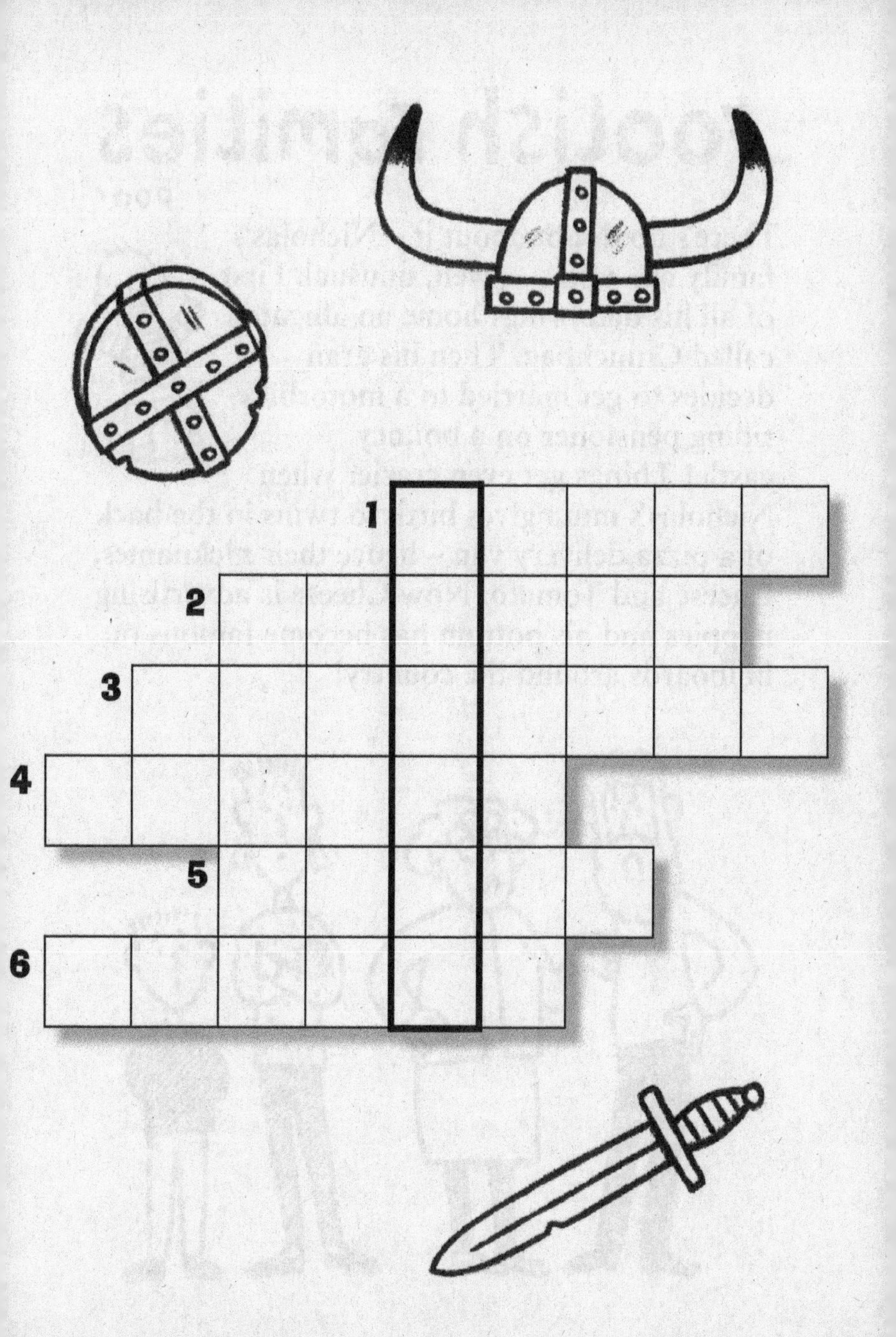
1
2
3
4
5
6

Foolish Families

POO!

There's no doubt about it – Nicholas's family are a bit . . . well, unusual. First of all his dad brings home an alligator called Crunchbag. Then his gran decides to get married to a motorbike-riding pensioner on a bouncy castle! Things get even crazier when Nicholas's mum gives birth to twins in the back of a pizza delivery van – hence their nicknames, Cheese and Tomato. Now Cheese is advertising nappies and his bottom has become famous on billboards around the country!

Dippy Dads

I don't think Mum is very happy about having an alligator in the house. She hates things with lots of teeth. (She can't even bear to look at Grannie's falsies when she puts them in cleaning fluid overnight!)

My Dad's got an Alligator!

What card game do Dad and the alligator like playing?
Snap!

What does Dad give the alligator to eat?
A crunch box.

What music do Dad and the alligator listen to?
Croc'n'roll.

Giggles with Granny

Yurrgh! I don't believe it – my granny's in love! She's at least five thousand years old (well, sixty-two, really) and she's gone all soppy about this man next door.

My Granny's Great Escape

Why are Gran's false teeth like stars?
They come out at night.

What time does a granny go to bed?
Three hours after she falls asleep on the sofa.

What's grey and goes up, down, up, down?
A granny on a bouncy castle.

Babies and bottoms

'Goodness gracious, all we seem to talk about in this house nowadays is poo and bottoms. I'm fed up with it all.'

My Brother's Famous Bottom Gets Pinched

Do Cheese and Tomato like nursery rhymes?
They prefer poo-ems.

What happened when Cheese and Tomato crawled under a cow?
They both got a pat on the head.

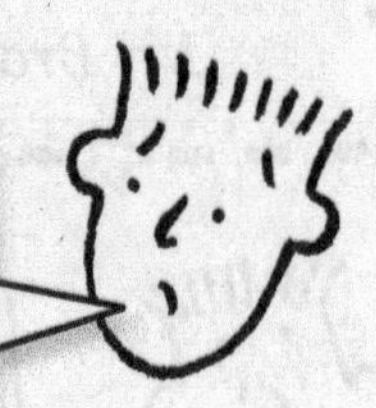

What happens when Cheese and Tomato come into the room?
You get double trouble.

Why are Cheese and Tomato being signed up for a football team?
They're always dribbling.

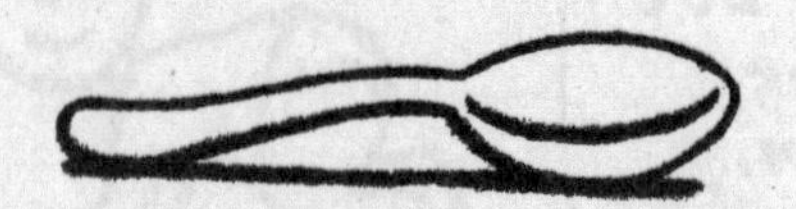

What did one full nappy say to the other?
'Just who do you stink you are?'

What did one stinky nappy say to the other?
'You're so full of yourself.'

What's the only kind of poo that doesn't smell horrible?
Shampoo.

What do Cheese and Tomato say when they've got dirty nappies?
'Poo-hoo!'

Big Bag Blunder

Oh no! Everything's fallen out of Cheese and Tomato's changing bag and is mixed up with Nicholas's school stuff. Can you help Nicholas by finding his school things and circling them?

Nappy Trail

Baby Cheese really needs to have his nappy put on, otherwise there might be a very smelly accident! Can you help him find the right trail?

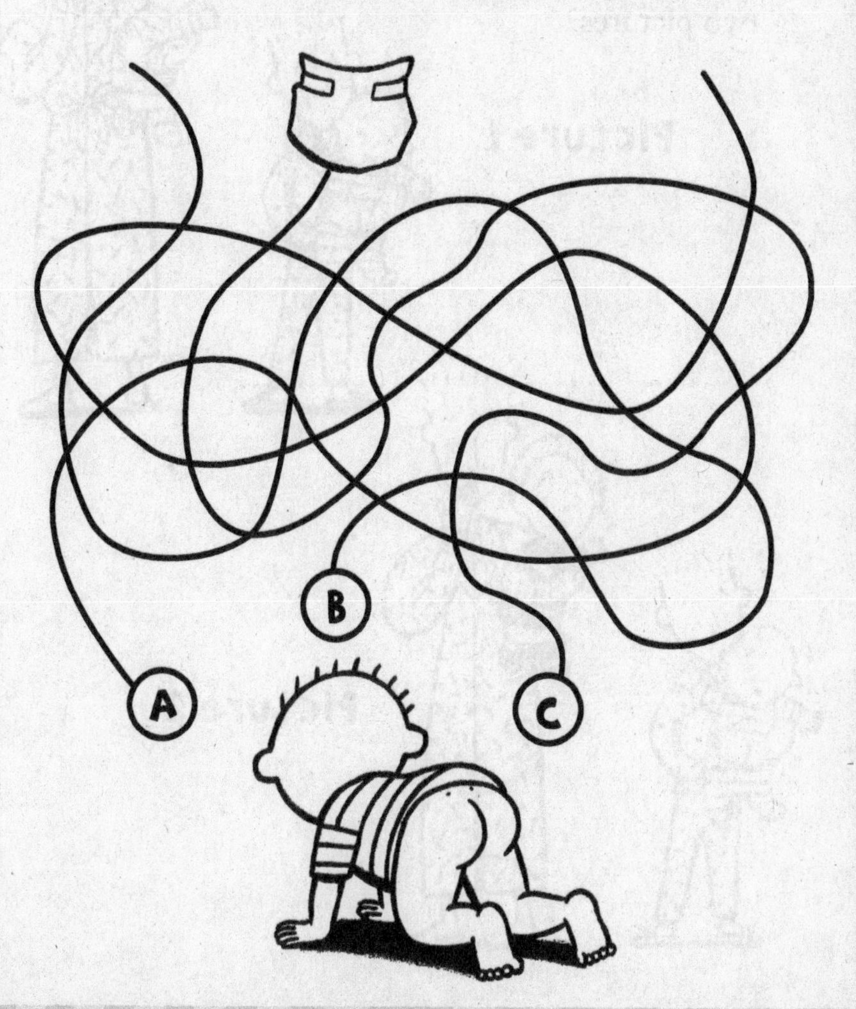

Spot the Difference

Nicholas and his mum have been left holding the babies! Can you spot six differences between the two pictures?

Picture 1

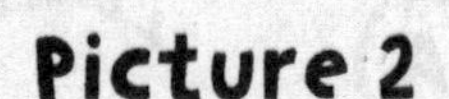

Suffering Superheroes

Kow Kraziness

Jamie Frink wants to be a famous film director so he decides to invent a new superhero to be the star of his movie – the one and only Krazy Kow!

ZOOM!!

She's fantastic, Krazy Kow. She's got a lumpy head, a lumpy back and wobbly lumps underneath. She can talk too, and she's got a Swiss Army udder. She has, really! You know what a Swiss Army penknife is like, with lots of gadgets? Well, Krazy Kow's udder doesn't just squirt milk. She also has a flame-thrower, rocket-launcher, water cannon, high-beam spotlight, mega-powerful vacuum cleaner and mirror for checking her make-up. (Plus a small prongy thing for getting stones out of horses' hoofs.)

Krazy Kow Saves The World – Well, Almost

What was the world like before Krazy Cow came along?
Udder chaos.

Where does Krazy Cow go for her holidays?
Moo York.

What's got a Swiss Army udder and goes 'Oom'?
Krazy Cow walking backwards.

How does Krazy Cow work out her sums?
On a cow-culator.

How does Krazy Cow relax in the evenings?
She goes to the moo-vies.

What happens when Krazy Cow gets caught in an earthquake?
You get a milkshake.

What kind of jumpers does Krazy Cow like wearing?
Jerseys.

Knock-knock.

Who's there?

Cowsgo.

Cowsgo who?

No, silly, cows go 'Moo'!

Laughs with Lightning Lucy

From crazy cows to flying females – meet Lucy King. She's a girl with extra-special powers – she can zoom through the air like a streak of lightning, flying from one amazing adventure to another!

Why does Lucy eat a lot of minestrone?
She's a girl with souper powers.

Why do they call her Lightning Lucy?
Because she's always there in a flash.

What's Lightning Lucy's favourite day of the week?
Flyday.

What do you get if you cross Lightning Lucy with a computer?
A screen saver.

Why does Lightning Lucy never stay for long?
She only does flying visits.

What does Lucy watch after school?
Sky TV.

Knock-knock.

Who's there?

Lucy.

Lucy who?

Lucy Lastic, your tights are falling down!

KK

Super Crossword

Test your superhero knowledge with this headscratching crossword!

ACROSS

4 All superheroes have special abilities. These are called _ _ _ _ _ _ _ _ _ _ _ _ _.

6 A lot of superheroes can do this. It's also something birds and planes can do!

DOWN

1 If a superhero wants to put on a disguise, he/she will wear this on their face.

2 Some superheroes wear this round their waist – you can clip your gadgets on to it.

3 This is part of a superhero's outfit. It flies out behind you when you are going fast.

5 Villains and baddies are usually this!

The Indoor Pirates and Heart-Ripper-Crunch-Munch-Smelly-Belly-Bum-Biter-Cuddles

Part Two: The best guard dog ever?

The pet shop owner, Mr Widgett, was surprised and a bit scared to see five pirates come marching into his shop. Mr Widgett was a small, hairy man and he was holding a small, hairy dog in his arms. The little dog had bright eyes and a pink tongue that stuck out.

'Can I help you?' asked Mr Widgett, putting the dog on the floor. It immediately began to bark and bounce up and down at the same time.

Captain Blackpatch eyed it with annoyance.

'We want a dog,' he declared. 'Not that titchy tiny kind of thing, but a proper dog.'

'A big one,' said Lumpy Lawson, holding a

hand above his head to show how big the dog should be.

'With big teeth,' added Polly.

'Big and sharp as sharks' teeth,' declared Molly.

Bald Ben gave Mr Widgett and the bouncy dog a friendly smile. 'I like that one,' he murmured.

The other four pirates turned and stared at Bald Ben. Captain Blackpatch shook his head and growled. 'That dog is about as big as a melon and about as much use.'

'Except you can eat melons,' Polly butted in.

'You can eat small dogs,' said Lumpy Lawson, which wasn't very nice of him at all. Mr Widgett let out a tiny, horrified squeak and Lumpy turned rather red. 'So I've been told,' he went on quickly. 'With gravy. I've never tried it myself.'

Mr Widgett cleared his throat carefully and said that, as it happened, he did have an Irish wolfhound, which was one of the biggest kinds of dog in the world. Captain Blackpatch nodded eagerly.

'A wolfhound, eh? That sounds just the job. A wolfhound! It must be very fierce if it's a wolfhound.'

'With big sharp teeth,' added Polly.

'I said that first,' Molly argued. 'I said sharp as sharks' teeth. Nurr.'

Mr Widgett brought in the wolfhound. The dog was truly large, almost as tall as Polly and Molly. The shaggy giant stood there and blinked brainlessly at them.

'Her name is Flower,' Mr Widgett told the pirates.

'Don't be ridiculous! You can't call a great big fierce dog like that Flower!' snorted the captain. 'We are going to call it Heart-Ripper.'

'Crunch-Munch!' said Lumpy.

'Smelly-Belly!' cried Molly.

'Bum-Biter!' yelled Polly.

Bald Ben looked at the huge, grey, shaggy wolfhound. 'Cuddles,' he said with a soft smile, and the big beast leaned up against the muscle-bound pirate and licked his hand.

Mr Widgett gave the pirates a couple of sacks of food and off they went back to the truck. With a lollop and a flollop Heart-Ripper-Crunch-Munch-Smelly-Belly-Bum-Biter-Cuddles leaped into the back. The Indoor Pirates clambered up after her and the wind blew through the dog's shaggy fur and big, floppy ears all the way home.

In the driving seat Captain Blackpatch smiled broadly. He knew it was going to be just brilliant when they got back to the house. They would be safe forever with their enormous burglar-biting guard dog.

The wolfhound soon made itself at home at number 25 Dolphin Street. First of all, it sniffed its way to the kitchen. On the way there it knocked over the coat stand in the hallway, swept the telephone off the table with its waggy tail and crashed through the kitchen doorway so hard that the door smashed into the wall and made a picture fall off and break on the floor.

'Stop it!' yelled Captain Blackpatch. 'I've only just tidied everything up!'

'*We* did the tidying!' shouted Polly.

'Exactly,' added Lumpy, and the pirates glared at their captain.

Blackpatch grunted and grumbled and finally pointed out that the other pirates had only done the tidying up because he had told them to, so really he should get the credit.

Meanwhile, Heart-Ripper-Crunch-Munch-Smelly-Belly-Bum-Biter-Cuddles was steadily eating her way through breakfast, lunch, tea, supper and all food stops in between. By the time she had finished the kitchen floor was covered in ripped packets and chewed shreds of cardboard. Food lay scattered in every direction.

'Now look what you've done!' Captain Blackpatch clutched his hat in despair. The dog gazed at him vacantly, licked her chops, wandered into the lounge and threw herself on the sofa. The sofa was so surprised that it fell over backwards, and there the two of them lay – the sofa and the dog – and Heart-Ripper-Crunch-Munch-Smelly-Belly-Bum-Biter-Cuddles went to sleep.

And snored.

VERY LOUDLY.

Captain Blackpatch folded his arms and gazed at the wolfhound. 'That beast is going to be a very good guard dog,' he said determinedly. 'Now we shall be able to sleep safe in our beds, which reminds me that I need some sleep myself. You lot tidy up while I go upstairs and have a rest. I'm worn out.'

'But you've only been up an hour or so, Captain,' said Bald Ben.

'Ben, I have been *thinking* and thinking is very tiring. Good night.'

'Good *morning*,' said Polly pointedly.

'Good afternoon,' Molly contradicted.

Captain Blackpatch disappeared upstairs while the remainder of the Indoor Pirates tidied up, again. They had just finished when their new wonder guard dog woke up. Heart-Ripper-Crunch-Munch-Smelly-Belly-Bum-Biter-Cuddles got to her feet, stretched her long body and knocked over two dining chairs. Then she decided to go exploring.

The dog wandered out into the hallway and headed up the stairs. The four pirates grinned at each other. Their brave captain was up there, asleep. They crept up the stairs behind the wolfhound so that they could see what was going to happen next.

Heart-Ripper-Crunch-Munch-Smelly-Belly-Bum-Biter-Cuddles went into the bathroom and tried eating the soap. She didn't like it so she spat it on to the floor in several chewed-up, useless lumps. She climbed into the tub, dumped the towels from the towel rail into the bath and somehow managed to turn on the shower.

In the next few seconds several things happened. The dog got soaked, the towels got soaked, the dog tried to jump out of the bath but slipped on the wet sides and fell over. She rolled about getting even wetter and finally managed to heave herself out of the tub. Then she fled from that nasty room where it rained all the time and headed straight for Captain Blackpatch's bedroom.

Heart-Ripper-Crunch-Munch-Smelly-Belly-Bum-Biter-Cuddles burst through the door without even opening it. The panels splintered into a thousand fragments of wood. The dog hurled

herself on to the bed and immediately began to roll about, frantically trying to get herself dry.

Captain Blackpatch was struggling beneath the weight of the bedraggled dog and the whole thing turned into a gigantic wrestling match.

'Help!' yelled the captain. 'Save me!'

'WOOF!' went the dog and promptly sat on his face.

'Gerroff! You're suffocating me!' squawked Captain Blackpatch.

'WOOF!' repeated the wolfhound.

'And don't bark in my ear, it hurts!'

'WOOF!'

They struggled and fought and barked and shouted until at last the bed legs broke, the bed crashed to the ground and both dog and pirate rolled on to the floor. By this time the captain's bedroom had turned into a huge tangled, mangled pile of sheets and blankets, with muddy paw marks going in every direction.

In the end, it was Bald Ben who saved the day. He waded into the mess, grabbed the wolfhound with his muscly arms and pulled her from the wreckage. Ben carried the hound downstairs and outside to the truck. He dumped her in the back. The other pirates trooped out, followed at length by a very dishevelled and angry, but silent, captain.

Blackpatch drove them all straight back to the pet shop. Mr Widgett looked at the pirates in surprise, while the little hairy, bouncy dog did a lot of bouncing and barking and wagged his tail very hard at Bald Ben and tried to leap into his arms.

'This wolfhound is useless,' snapped the captain. 'I have never come across such a useless, dopey dog. We want a different one.'

'This one,' smiled Bald Ben, because by this time the bouncy dog had finally managed to jump into his arms. It was of course the dog that Bald Ben had wanted all along.

And so the pirates left Heart-Ripper-Crunch-Munch-Smelly-Belly-Bum-Biter-Cuddles at the shop and took their new small dog home, where she soon settled in and proved to be a very good guard dog indeed – despite her size.

Captain Blackpatch told the other pirates to tidy up the house but this time they refused. So the captain had to sort out the bathroom and his bedroom while the others stayed with their new small dog downstairs and tried to think of a good name.

'Bouncer,' suggested Lumpy Lawson.

'Smelly-Belly,' said Molly.

'You said that last time, stupid,' snapped Polly. 'Bum-Biter is much better.'

'You said *that* last time,' argued Molly. 'Stupid yourself.'

The twins argued and Bald Ben gazed fondly at the little dog nestling in his lap, with his tongue still sticking out.

'Cuddles,' said Bald Ben firmly. 'Without all those other bits we had before. Just Cuddles.'

And they all went to sleep.

(Except for Captain Blackpatch, who was still tidying up, and besides, his bed was broken.)

THE END

Alien Antics

There's something very odd about the new family who've moved in across the road. They behave strangely, have weird penetrating eyes – and Rob is sure he's seen a UFO hovering over their house. There's only one answer – the Vorks must be aliens! What if they're here to take over the Earth? And how can Rob save the world when nobody believes him?

I knew they were aliens the first moment I saw them. I could feel it in my body. I got this kind of creeping sensation, as if ants were slowly crawling up and down the inside of my bones.

I'm Telling You, They're Aliens!

What would you do if a one-legged alien knocked at your door?
Tell him to hop it.

Why should you never insult an alien?
Because you might hurt his feelers.

What should you do if you meet a blue alien?
Try and cheer it up.

What should you do if you meet a green alien?
Wait until it's ripe.

Why did the alien leave the party?
Because there was no atmosphere.

Where do aliens park their spaceships?
At parking meteors.

What is the aliens' favourite board game?
Moon-opoly.

Mum, Mum, where's our dinner?

Be quiet, you lot – I've only got four pairs of hands.

What are aliens' favourite sweets?
Mars-mallows.

Why are aliens so scary?
Because they're extra-terror-estrials.

What's an alien's favourite day of the week?
Moonday.

What do aliens cook their eggs in?
An Unidentified Frying Object.

What's tasty, crunchy and travels at 1,000 kilometres an hour?
A space chip.

What do aliens spread on their toast?
Mars-malade.

What live on other planets and are covered in tomato sauce?
Beans from outer space.

Where do aliens catch their trains?
At the space station.

What did the alien say to the garden?
'Take me to your weeder!'

What did the alien say to the magazine rack?
'Take me to your reader!'

Space Search

Can you find these space-related words in the wordsearch below? They may go up, down, diagonally and even backwards.

I	G	X	K	V	D	E	T	S
S	P	A	C	E	S	H	I	P
T	E	W	L	G	P	M	H	L
A	D	U	P	A	G	I	C	A
R	Q	M	L	U	X	W	F	N
C	H	I	S	V	G	Y	J	E
U	E	F	U	C	O	M	E	T
N	O	O	M	O	T	A	I	B

ALIEN
MOON
COMET
GALAXY
SPACESHIP
STAR
PLANET

Alien Message

What are the aliens in this spaceship trying to say to us? Find out by crossing out all the letters that appear twice in the spaceship. Then unscramble the letters that are left to get the message. Write it below.

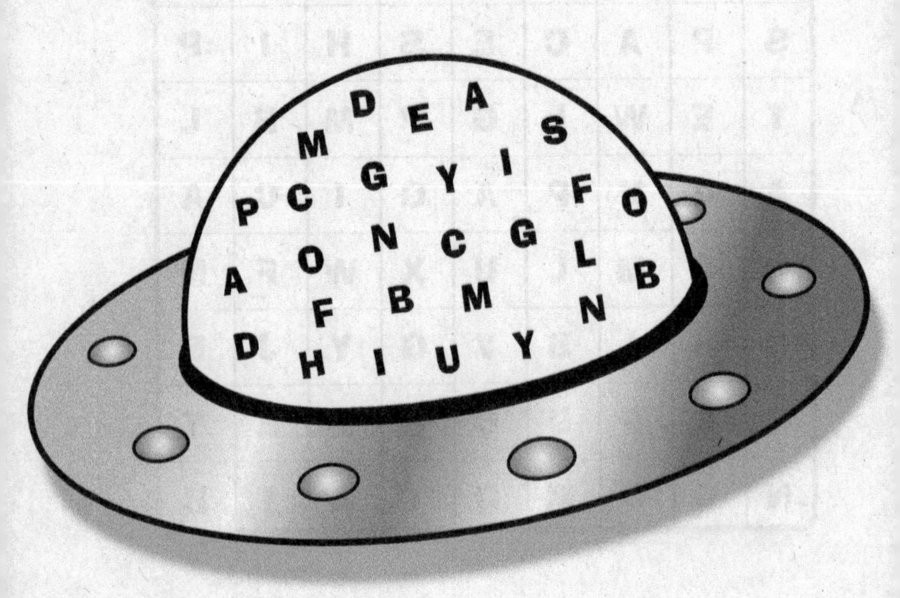

_ _ _ _   _ _ !

Puzzling Planets

Rob is convinced that aliens are living out there in space. Take a look at the planets of our solar system and see if you can complete their names using only vowels – a, e, i, o or u.

M_rs

_ _rth

J_p_t_r

_r_n_s

M_rc_ry

S_t_rn

V_n_s

N_pt_n_

Giant Guffaws

When Giant Jim comes to town, people are terrified they'll be eaten or squashed. But Jim is actually a good giant who only means well. Unfortunately, he just can't seem to do anything right – and he's so big he seems to cause nothing but trouble!

'Do you think you could speak more softly?' asked Mrs Goodbody. 'Every time you speak it makes a terrible wind and we all fall over. And please don't sneeze.'

'Sorry,' said the giant, and everyone fell over.

'Sorry,' he said again, very quietly, and everyone picked themselves up.

Giant Jim and the Hurricane

What should you do if Giant Jim sits on your car?
Get a new one.

How do you know if Giant Jim's under your bed?
Your bed is touching the ceiling.

Why did Giant Jim buy a new pair of shoes?
He was too big for his boots.

How can you tell if Giant Jim's in your fridge?
You can't shut the door.

Where are giants found?
They're so big they're hardly ever lost.

How does Giant Jim stop his trainers from smelling?
Ogre-eaters.

What is higher than Giant Jim?
Giant Jim's hat!

Where do you find giant snails?
At the end of a giant's fingers.

What's a giant's favourite ball game?
Squash.

What do you call a giant in a phone box?
Stuck.

Gigantic Word Grid

See how giant your brain is by trying this tricky word grid. If you get the answers right, you'll find the name of a different kind of giant in the vertical box.

1 Giant Jim isn't short. In fact, he's very ____.

2 This golden musical instrument was owned by the giant from *Jack and the Beanstalk*.

3 If a giant wanted to stomp on you, he would probably use his big ____.

4 If Giant Jim fell into a lake, you would hear a very loud one of these!

5 Another word that means 'big'.

Whopping Words

Can you find – and circle – six words that would describe Giant Jim?

big tiny little huge small medium mini enormous gigantic short massive large teeny

Giant Changes

Can you turn a giant into a plate? Read each question and write the new word, changing only one or two letters each time. All the words have five letters.

G I A N T

_ _ _ _ _ Fairies and godmothers sometimes _ _ _ _ _ wishes to lucky humans. Change one letter.

_ _ _ _ _ Change one letter to get a noise pigs make.

_ _ _ _ _ Change two letters to get a word that is the opposite of 'sharp'.

_ _ _ _ _ Change two letters to get something that grows.

_ _ _ _ _ Change one letter to get something that flies.

_ _ _ _ _ Change one letter to get something you eat your food from.

Kicking Karate

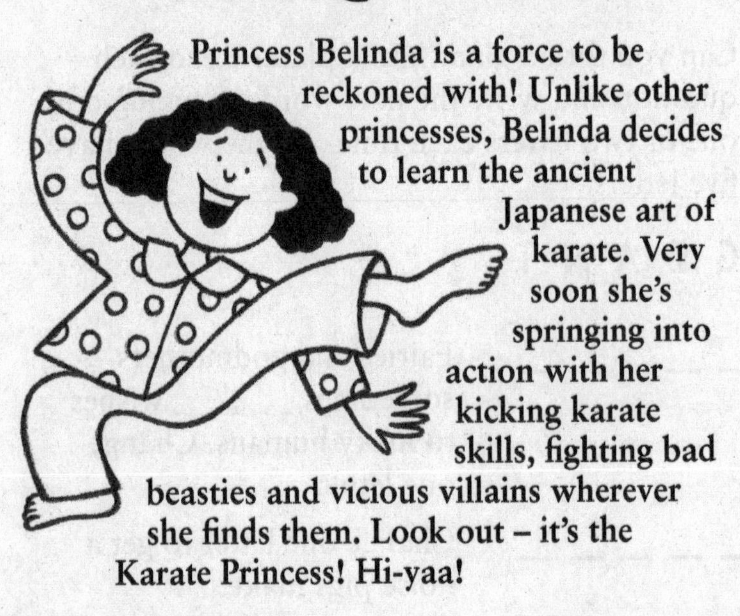

Princess Belinda is a force to be reckoned with! Unlike other princesses, Belinda decides to learn the ancient Japanese art of karate. Very soon she's springing into action with her kicking karate skills, fighting bad beasties and vicious villains wherever she finds them. Look out – it's the Karate Princess! Hi-yaa!

'Aaaaa-HA!' She gave a great yell, spun round on one foot and launched her other foot at the centre of the statue. There was a splinter of breaking stone and the statue cracked into two separate halves. Even as the top section toppled to the floor, Belinda raised her right arm and sliced the head off with a single blow of her bare hand.

The Karate Princess

What does Belinda shout when she's being pushed on a swing?
'Hi-yaa! Hi-yaa!'

How do baddies feel when they first meet Belinda?
They're completely thrown.

What is the Karate Princess's favourite meal?
Fish and chops.

Does Belinda like doing the same things as her sisters?
No – they go shopping, Belinda goes chopping.

Does the Karate Princess like windy days?
Yes, she enjoys a good blow.

What's Belinda's idea of a good time?
A kicking party!

What do you call the Karate Princess's dad?
King Fu.

What's Belinda teaching her pet pig?
Pork chops.

What happened when Princess Belinda burped during karate practice?
She gave herself a royal pardon.

Kicking Karate Wordsearch

Hi-yaa! Princess Belinda's on the warpath with her kicking karate moves. Can you find the karate-related words in the wordsearch below? The words may go up, down, diagonally or even backwards.

O	P	U	R	C	R	I
P	U	N	C	H	B	C
L	M	E	W	O	P	T
K	I	U	O	P	I	H
I	K	A	J	N	U	R
C	H	U	L	E	L	O
K	R	T	B	L	O	W

KICK
THROW
PUNCH
CHOP
RUN
BLOW
JUMP

Puzzling Princesses

Belinda is *very* unusual for a princess – you don't usually find kings' daughters aiming chops and kicks at villains! But how much do you know about other famous princesses? Test your knowledge with the quiz below.

1 This sleepy princess can only be awoken by the kiss of her one true love.

The _ _ _ _ _ _ _ _ _ _ _ _ _ _ _ _ _ _

2 This story is about a princess who had an uncomfortable night sleeping on a huge pile of mattresses.

The Princess and the _ _ _

3 This princess was imprisoned in a tall tower and grew her hair very long.

_ _ _ _ _ _ _ _ _

4 This story is about a princess who made a promise to a slimy creature – who turned out to be a handsome prince!

The Princess and the _ _ _ _

Accidents and 'Jackcidents'

What is it with Jack? He's so accident-prone that he seems to live in the casualty department. Only Jack could sit on a fork and get it stuck in his bottom. Ouch!

Only Jack could crash into a load of tinned tomatoes, then get knocked off his bike by a car . . . so it's back to hospital for Jack!

Mum says I'm a walking disaster. Dad says I don't have accidents. 'You're an accident waiting to happen, Jack,' he told me. 'In fact, you *are* an accident.'

'A Jackcident,' sniggered my little bro Ben.

Beware! Killer Tomatoes

Nurse, I've just swallowed the film from my camera!

Well, let's wait and see what develops.

Doctor, I've broken my arm in two places.

Well, don't go back there again, then!

Nurse, I've been stung by a bee. Shall I put some ointment on it?

Don't be silly – it must be miles away by now.

Doctor, I've just swallowed a mouth organ.

Think yourself lucky you don't play the piano.

Nurse, how can I cure my sleepwalking?

Sprinkle drawing pins on your bedroom floor.

Nurse, I've got terrible wind. Can you give me something?

Yes – here's a kite.

Doctor, I can't get to sleep.

Lie on the edge of the bed and you'll soon drop off.

Nurse, I keep seeing double.

Just take a seat.
Which one?

Doctor, you have to help me out!

Certainly, which way did you come in?

Killer Memory Test

Jack: Doctor, I've lost my memory!
Doctor: When did this happen?
Jack: When did *what* happen?

See if your memory is better than Jack's with this tricky test! Study the picture while counting to thirty. Then cover it up with another book or piece of paper, making sure you can't see the picture. Now try and answer the questions below.

1 Jack's right leg is in plaster. **True/False**
2 Jack's pyjamas are spotty. **True/False**
3 Two people are wearing glasses. **True/False**
4 Everyone looks worried. **True/False**
5 Jack is sucking his thumb. **True/False**

Which Jack?

Oh no! Jack's come off his bike again! Look carefully at the four pictures below – which one is different?

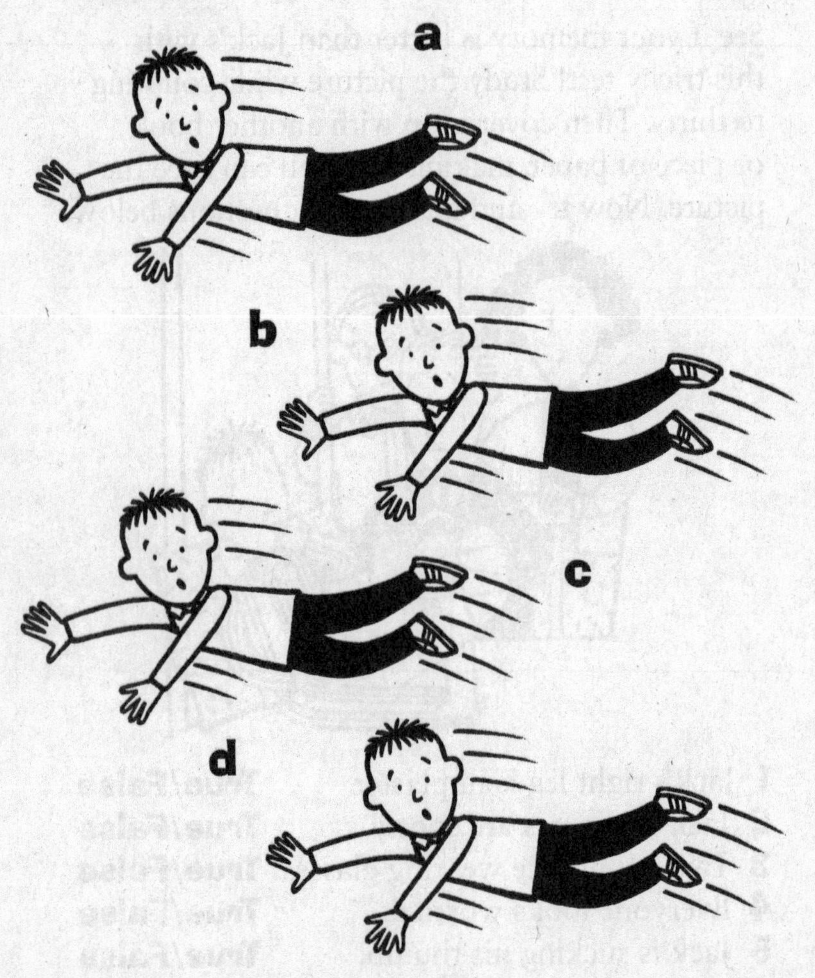

Seasonal Silliness

Did you know that Father Christmas had a bad brother? And that he once plotted to turn everyone in the world into zombies – using Christmas puddings?!

The *Death Pudding* is a gigantic, slowly revolving Christmas pudding. Engulfed in flames, it spins through Deep Space. This is home for Bad Christmas, a home as big as a football stadium. This is where he plots and plans. He is going to take over the world. But first of all he has to exterminate his brother and take his place.

Yes! He is going to DESTROY FATHER CHRISTMAS!

Invasion of the Christmas Puddings

Luckily for us, his evil plan is foiled by a group of courageous children and their teacher, Miss Comet. Father Christmas rules again! Hurrah!

Why does Father Christmas go down the chimney?
Because it soots him.

What do you get if you cross a detective with Father Christmas?
Santa Clues.

What do the elves give Father Christmas when he's finished delivering the presents?
Santapplause!

Why does Father Christmas have three gardens?
So he can hoe, hoe, hoe.

What goes red, white, red, white?
Father Christmas rolling down a hill.

What do you say to Father Christmas when he is taking the register at school?
'Present!'

What do you get if you cross Father Christmas with a duck?
Christmas quackers.

What is the name of Father Christmas's cat?
Santa Paws.

How does Father Christmas take pictures?
With his North Pole-aroid.

What do the elves sing to Father Christmas?
'Freeze a jolly good fellow!'

How many chimneys does Father Christmas go down?
Stacks!

What does Father Christmas write on his Christmas cards?
ABCDEFGHIJK MNOPQRST UVWXYZ (No L).

Puddings and Pies

Mmm! Christmas wouldn't be the same without all those tasty treats. And there's no way Bad Christmas is going to get his hands on these ones! Can you match up the words to find the treats?

mince	**turkey**
roast	**sauce**
Christmas	**butter**
cranberry	**log**
yule	**pie**
brandy	**pudding**

Spot the Difference

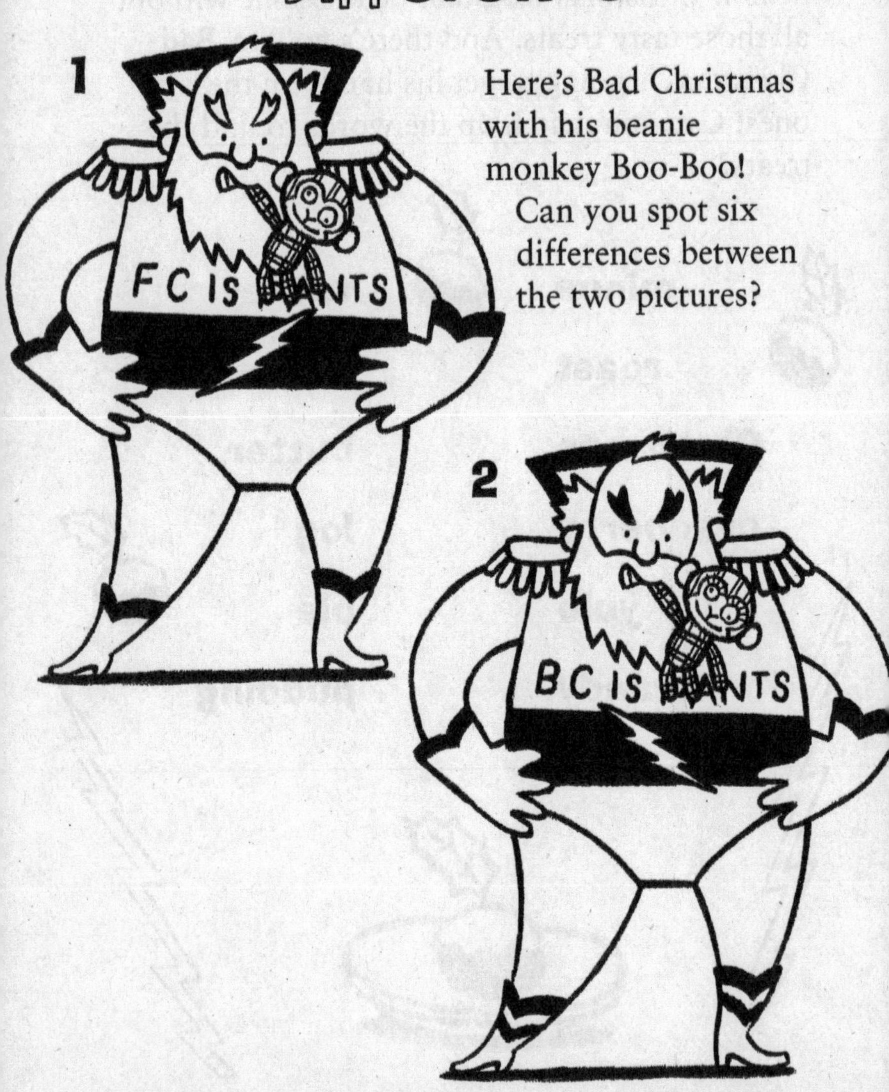

Here's Bad Christmas with his beanie monkey Boo-Boo!

Can you spot six differences between the two pictures?

Ridiculous Rhymes

Now you've come to the end of the book, you'll know all about a whole host of crazy characters. But can you find the correct word to complete these equally crazy rhymes?

1 Look! There's Streaker running past.
Did you see her? She's so _ _ _ _.

2 Most pirates try their very best
To find a glittering treasure _ _ _ _ _.

3 Vikings were so big and strong,
Their swords were sharp; their boats were _ _ _ _.

4 There's Lightning Lucy in the sky.
Whoosh! That girl can really _ _ _.

5 Poor Jack is just a big disaster.
He broke his leg, now it's in _ _ _ _ _ _ _.

6 Giant Jim is very large.
His bottom's bigger than a _ _ _ _ _ .

ANSWERS

Hundred-Mile-an-Hour Hilarity

Streaker Scramble: nose, eye, ear, tongue, paw, tail.
Streaker Shapes: 1. F, 2. D, 3. A, 4. E, 5. C, 6. B.
Fast or Slow? 1. Cheetah 2. Antelope 3. Greyhound 4. Rabbit 5. Tortoise 6. Snail

Animal Antics

Animal Wordsnake: see right

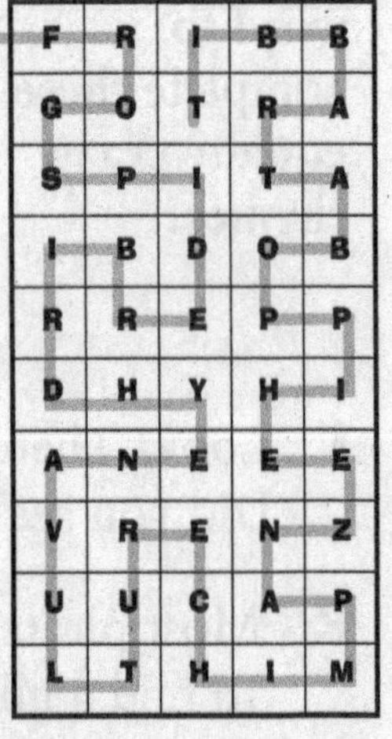

Puppies, Kittens and more . . .
1. d 2. g 3. a 4. i
5. c 6. h 7. f 8. b 9. e

Dippy Dinosaurs

Dino True or False: 1. True
2. True 3. True 4. False.
5. True 6. False – we have discovered hundreds of species of dinosaur but there are probably still more out there.
Dino-words: Here are some of the words we found. Did you find any others?
ON, IN, AN, SUN, SON, SIR, SAD, RUN, DIN, ROD, OUR, OAR, NOD, AIR, AND, SOUR, SOAR, SAND, SAID, ROAD, RAIN, SARI, RAID, IRON, SOUND, ROUND, RADIO, DRAIN, AROUND
Dinosaur Match: 1. b 2. a 3. c 4. d

Pirate Pandemonium

Crow's-Nest Climb: parrot
Swashbuckling Crossword: see right
Pirate Know-How: 1. gold 2. rum 3. hat 4. eye patch 5. fight 6. sail.

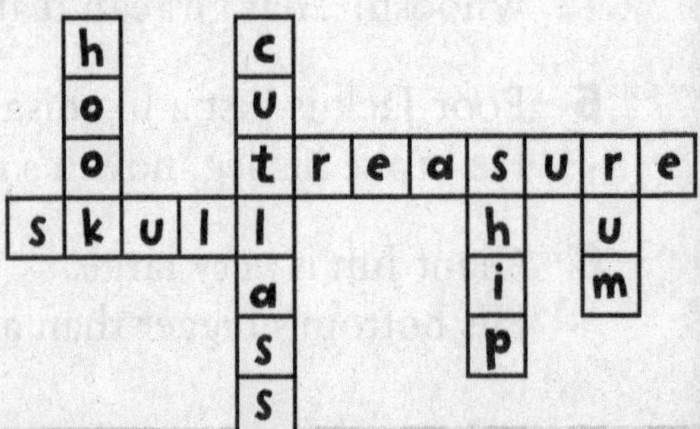

Potty Pharaohs

Egyptian Odd-One-Out: 1. c 2. a 3. b 4. c
Sennapod's Treasure Trail: see right

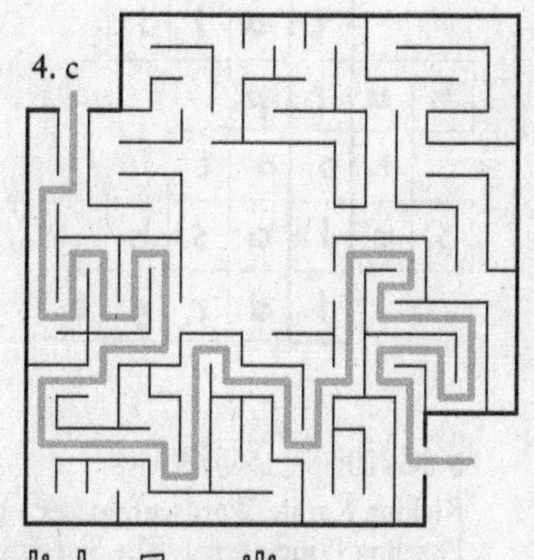

Vagrant Vikings

Viking Word Grid: see below

				s	w	o	r	d
		s	h	i	e	l	d	
	l	o	n	g	b	o	a	t
a	r	m	o	u	r			
		h	o	r	n	s		
b	e	a	r	d				

Foolish Families

Big Bag Blunder: Nicholas's things are: pencil, pen, ruler, trainers, key ring, rubber, homework, library book.
Nappy Trail: Answer is C.
Spot the Difference: In picture 2: 1. Nicholas's slippers have got pom-poms on them. 2. There is no belt/bow on Mum's gown. 3. There are no polka dots on Nicholas's left sleeve. 4. The baby Mum is holding has got black and white stripes on his suit. 5. The baby Nicholas is holding is bald. 6. Nicholas is smiling!

Suffering Superheroes

Super Crossword: see right

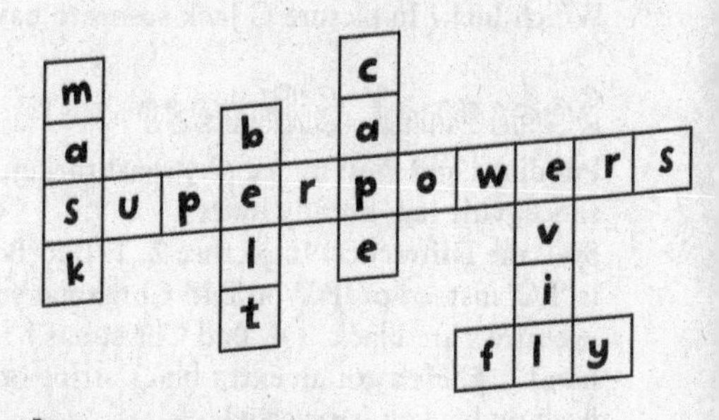

I	G	X	K	V	D	E	T	S
S	P	A	C	E	S	H	I	P
T	E	W	L	G	P	M	H	L
A	D	U	P	A	G	I	C	A
R	Q	M	L	U	X	W	F	N
C	H	I	S	V	G	Y	J	E
U	E	F	U	C	O	M	E	T
N	O	O	M	O	T	A	I	B

Alien Antics

Space Search: see left
Alien Message: The message says 'Help Us!'
Puzzling Planets: Mars, Earth, Jupiter, Uranus, Mercury, Saturn, Venus, Neptune.

		t	a	l	l	
h	a	r	p			
	f	o	o	t		
s	p	l	a	s	h	
		l	a	r	g	e

Giant Guffaws

Gigantic Word Grid: see left
Whopping Words: big, huge, enormous, gigantic, massive, large.
Giant Changes: GIANT – GRANT – GRUNT – BLUNT – PLANT – PLANE – PLATE

O	P	U	R	C	R	I
P	U	N	C	H	B	C
L	M	E	W	O	P	T
K	I	U	O	P	I	H
I	K	A	J	N	U	R
C	H	U	L	E	L	O
K	R	T	B	L	O	W

Kicking Karate

Kicking Karate Wordsearch: see right
Puzzling Princesses: 1. The Sleeping Beauty 2. The Princess and the Pea 3. Rapunzel 4. The Princess and the Frog

Accidents and 'Jackcidents'

Killer Memory Test: 1. True 2. False – the pyjamas are striped. 3. False – only one person is wearing glasses. 4. True 5. False – Jack has got his finger in his mouth.
Which Jack? In picture C Jack seems to have lost one of his fingers!

Seasonal Silliness

Puddings and Pies: mince pie, roast turkey, Christmas pudding, cranberry sauce, yule log, brandy butter.
Spot the Difference: In picture 2: 1. Boo-Boo has got eyelashes. 2. There is 'BC' instead of 'FC' on Bad Christmas's suit. 3. Bad Christmas's eyebrows are black. 4. Bad Christmas has only three fingers on his left hand. 5. He's got an extra black stripe on his boots. 6. The lightning flash on his belt is reversed.
Ridiculous Rhymes: 1. fast 2. chest 3. long 4. fly 5. plaster 6. barge